Editorial and project management by
Shaila Shah, BAAF
Designed by Andrew Haig & Associates
Illustrations by Sarah Rawlings
Printed by The Lavenham Press, Suffolk

Tina's STORY

CW00958478

Children and families come in all shapes and sizes! Let's hear about some of them. When you read Tina's story, can you see if you can find her in the playground?

Introduction

When children are separated from their family of origin part of their very self is in jeopardy. No matter what their age or circumstances, that interruption of familiar and uniquely personal kinship ties can lead to potentially lifelong wounds. Adoption and fostering is not only about joining and welcoming, but also about grieving and losing as well as struggling and working together. Family life is never easy and new or reconstituted families have additional pressures and demands.

One of these is to help children to make sense of their often fragmented and confused experience. Their past is a crucial part of who they are and one of the key tasks for carers is to help children to integrate their past and their present. They are then able to move towards a future that builds on reality including the joys and sorrows which characterise all our stories. This task is not easy. So often the implicit message to permanent carers is to treat the child as if he or she were their own – and indeed that is necessary in order to build the quality of relationships that all parents hope for. Yet they are also asked never to forget that children are not their own – that they come from a different family with a different history.

Why this workbook?

The importance of helping children to make sense of their story is widely accepted. Each of us has a basic right to know who we are and where we come from. Children who cannot understand why they are separated will almost always take on the guilt and responsibility themselves. It is therefore vital that they are helped to make sense of their individual history. Life story books are valuable tools in this respect, but care needs to be taken that they are not reduced to little more than photograph albums. Children want to know not only what, but why, and information needs to be accurate, truthful, respectful and age/development appropriate.

This workbook is one amongst a collection relating to a number of children who are not living with their birth families. The stories each have a different scenario and it is hoped that they may act as useful triggers in a variety of settings. Experience shows that the reality of getting down to discussing and explaining is far from easy. Birth families, foster carers, adopters and social workers all struggle with the language and feelings involved. For birth families the pain and loss that is inherent in relinquishment can be overwhelming. Permanent carers can be fearful and avoidant of genuinely confronting a history which is not part of their shared experience. Social workers may be over-protective regarding difficult information and often feel lacking in communication skills. Therefore it is imperative that in order to use this workbook most effectively the reader is adequately prepared for the task.

Preparation

It is important to recognise that exploring painful and traumatic events with children evokes for each of us our own experience of loss or suffering. Learning to live with these events may be a lifelong task but we need at least to be on the journey before we can help a child to risk setting out. If there are areas of our life that remain too difficult to face we may need more time before embarking on working with children. Our fear, hesitancy or reluctance to face pain may well communicate itself to the child who will sense that difficult issues are best left unspoken and kept inside.

Some children may be overwhelmed by their experience, struggling with guilt, anger, sadness, responsibility, divided loyalties, and unsure of their capacity to survive emotionally. A sensitive, caring adult can acknowledge these feelings with the child, accepting but not minimising their confusion and hurt. Demonstrating a strength and resilience in the face of pain allows the child slowly to develop a sense of hope and conviction that all will be well. The stories in this series are about facts, but also about feelings, for the two cannot be separated. Adults need to be honest about their own emotions before they are able to help children with theirs.

In order to share a child's history it is essential to have as much accurate information as possible about their circumstances. Different tools may help to identify gaps in knowledge that ideally need to filled before embarking on life history work. For a fuller and more detailed account see BAAF's book, *Life Story Work*.

A *word of caution*

Some children with particularly difficult and traumatic histories may be unable for a variety of reasons to confront their past. Care should be exercised when children appear to be well defended and highly resistant to sharing previous experience. Sometimes such children may be receiving therapeutic help to explore painful issues and this may be a long-term process. Children – and adults – maintain their defences for a purpose and they deserve a healthy respect. These stories are potential channels whereby connections may be made, feelings shared, hopes and fears discussed and attachment encouraged. They should never be used in an intrusive way that fails to respect the child's wishes and anxieties. All adults can do is to open doors; it is the child who decides whether or not to pass through.

Using the workbook

The workbooks in this series are specific and are therefore inevitably limited in their direct application. Every story line is unique and there can be few common denominators. However, the range extends across a variety of familiar scenarios and backgrounds, and while they may require adjustment given individual circumstances, it is hoped that they may also be helpful triggers. In some cases carers or professionals may be able to use them as they stand; alternatively they may prove helpful in enabling adults to rehearse a specific story line that relates to a particular child, or children can be encouraged to note the differences/similarities between their own stories and those of the children featured.

Various tools have been incorporated into the story and the work sheets at the end are further aids to helping children explore issues and feelings. Both the work sheets and story can be used flexibly and can therefore be moved around in different combinations. It will be important for adults to consider the individual needs of each child. The workbook reflects a multicultural population and many children will require additional information concerning, for example, their racial, cultural and religious heritage; preverbal children will be more able to identify with play techniques and very simple story lines; learning disabled children may make greater use of visual content than the written word. Each child will have his or her own needs and story and the workbook is meant to be used creatively and flexibly in conjunction with the many other useful tools already available.

Birth parents, carers and social workers may find the story lines helpful to use with children as part of preparation work, within family placements, or at key times such as adoption hearings or disruption. Specific (future) stories may be helpful to families preparing their own children for adoption or fostering, stepfamilies who are adopting and those who may be helping their children to understand relinquishment of a sibling. Guardians, residential workers, family centres and day nurseries may find relevant scenarios that could be useful in their work with children and young people and there is an educational value in raising community awareness of children's needs and the range of situations represented within adoption and fostering.

Explaining and exploring

Life is a continual story and the task of story telling is never complete. As the child grows and develops so too will his or her understanding of their situation. Histories will need to be repeated, reworked and more carefully explained as comprehension becomes more sophisticated. It is important to use developmentally appropriate language and concepts and be aware of the need to refine and adapt material according to each child's needs and abilities. It is important to listen to children – to hear what it is they want to know and to avoid the temptation to convey too much too quickly. Stories evolve, often from short conversations about people, places, times, events. Children will often not need the elaborate explanations that adults prepare. Equally, it is dangerous to wait until children ask questions before imparting information; some never will and need permission to broach such personal issues. Such permission is not only verbal, but manifests itself in so many of our unspoken attitudes and responses to the child's history.

Visual aids such as this workbook are only one small contribution to the child's ongoing task of making sense of who they are. Direct and indirect contact with the child's family members can be a major source of information and encourage a realistic and developing understanding of what has happened and why. For permanently placed children the biggest factor will be their carer's ability to embrace both them and their history, knowing that they are one and the same. Our background may be complex and painful but sharing that experience over time within an environment of safety, acceptance and affirmation is the way to healing and emotional growth.

Tina's
STORY

Tina is 10 years old. She will soon be leaving Greenfield School. Tina's family are Mum, Dad, and her two brothers; Tom is 7 and Jason is 5. Tina is not living with her family right now.

This is Tina's story.

Tina misses her family and feels sad about not living with them. When she is upset Tina listens to her favourite pop music on her personal stereo. It helps her to forget just for a while.

Tina knew that things were not right at home, especially with Dad. She was always his favourite and loved their special times together. Dad told her stories and helped her with her schoolwork.

But as Tina grew older she sometimes had funny feelings when she was alone with Dad. She couldn't understand or talk about how she felt. All she knew was that the feelings made her uncomfortable. She wished they would go away.

Then one night Dad came into Tina's bedroom. He gave her a goodnight cuddle. Then he started to touch her **private parts**.

Tina didn't know what to do. She didn't want Dad to touch her like that. It made her feel bad inside, but Dad told her it was okay. He said it was his special way of loving her and that it was their secret.

Sometimes Tina pretended to be asleep hoping that Dad would not come into her room. But he did. He told Tina that she was very special. She didn't feel special. She felt bad and miserable. Tina wanted to tell her Mum about it, but she knew Dad would be angry if she shared the secret.

Tina got more and more upset and confused. When she was at school she found it difficult to do her work. Her teacher, Mrs Saunders, wondered what was wrong.

One day at school Mrs Saunders talked to the class about touching. She said that some **touches** make you feel safe and some touches make you feel funny and uncomfortable. Tina understood exactly what she meant.

Mrs Saunders said that everyone should be able to say 'no' to touches that made them unhappy and that it was okay to say 'no'.

Tina knew that Dad's touches made her feel very unhappy and she wondered if she had done something wrong.

She started to cry at break time and her friend, Ravinder, asked Tina what was wrong. Tina tried to explain about Dad's touches. Ravinder said she should tell a grown-up about it – someone she trusted. Tina was afraid to tell her Mum because Dad would be mad. She asked Ravinder to come with her to see Mrs Saunders.

Mrs Saunders told Tina that it was good she had been able to tell and she knew someone who would help.

Later that day, a **social worker**, Jan, and a policewoman came to see Tina at school. Jan told Tina that she was very brave to have told them about Dad and that it wasn't Tina's fault. Grown-ups shouldn't touch children in private places. Dad would have known that touching Tina like that was wrong.

Jan and the policewoman believed what Tina told them and said they would have to talk to Tina's Mum and Dad.

Later, Jan came back to school with Molly, a **foster carer**. Jan explained that Mum and Dad had said they didn't understand why Tina had said such things. Jan said she would talk to Mum and Dad some more. She thought it would be better for Tina if she stayed with Molly and her family, where she would be safe. Jan had told Molly about what had happened. Tina was glad because she didn't want to talk about it again. Jan had collected some of Tina's things from home and they all went to Molly's house in Jan's car.

Tina was very confused. She knew that Dad would be angry and she thought that Mum might be too. What would Tom and Jason think had happened to her? Tina didn't know what to do. She didn't want to go home and she didn't want to go to a strange place either. She wished it would all go away, but she knew it wouldn't.

Molly told Tina that she believed her and Tina started to feel better. Molly said that she was very sorry that this had happened to Tina but that she would be safe with them. She said grown-ups shouldn't touch children like that and that Tina was right to tell, even if things were hard now. She said that if Tina hadn't told, the touching would have carried on and probably got worse.

Molly's husband, Jim, and her daughters, Sally and Denise, were very friendly. But Tina felt strange being away from her family.

Jan spoke to Mum and Dad again. They said Tina was lying but Tina knew she wasn't. She felt mixed up and upset.

Molly said she knew Tina would have lots of different feelings about her family. She helped her to write down how she felt about different people.

Tina has been told that she will be staying in foster care. She sees Tom and Jason often when Jan brings them to visit. Jan has told Tina that she doesn't need to worry about her brothers. They have said that Dad hasn't touched them in the way he touched Tina. Sometimes mum visits too but that's not easy because she is still angry about things and so are Grandad and Grandma. Tina likes to see Mum but finds it hard. She'd like to see Dad too but he doesn't want to visit.

Tina knows she cannot go home because she won't be safe. Molly and Tina drew circles to show who Tina felt **safe** with and with whom she didn't.

Sometimes Tina still gets very sad and angry about what has happened and plays lots of music to take her mind off things.

But life is getting better. Tina is looking forward to starting at a new school next year and making new friends. She will be able to walk there with Sally and Denise but she may have to leave her personal stereo at home!

Tina knows that Molly cares about her and believes what she says. Tina's family will always be an important part of her life. But she knows that until her Mum believes her and her Dad gets help for his touching problem she will need to live in a foster home.

Fostering means Tina can live somewhere else with another family that will care for her while she grows up, but still see her family.

something to remember…

Sometimes we don't feel safe with the people that we love and live with. This can be confusing. When you don't feel safe, it is important to tell someone you trust how you feel.

special words

Private parts – the parts of our body that are personal and private and that other people don't touch.

Touches – some touches make us feel happy and safe but there are also touches that make us feel uncomfortable, sad or frightened.

A **social worker** is someone who tries to help children and their families when they are unhappy. They also try to find foster carers for children who cannot live with their family.

A **foster carer** is someone who looks after children who cannot live with their family. Young children usually stay for a while until they can go home or move on to a new family. Older children sometimes stay longer.

Safe – feeling safe is when you feel OK with someone and not scared or worried.

Worksheet

1 Who are the special people in your life?

Write down the feelings you have about each of them.

_____

_____

_____

_____

_____

_____

_____

_____

_____

2 If something was bothering you who would you talk to?

_____

_____

_____

3 If you are not living with your birth family do you understand why? Are there any questions you would like to ask?

_____

_____

_____

_____

_____

_____

4 When you get angry or upset what helps you to feel better?

_____

_____

_____

_____

_____

_____

_____

_____

5

What helps you feel safe?

_____

_____

_____

_____

_____

_____

_____

_____

_____

_____

_____

6

Who do you feel safe with?

_____

_____

_____

_____

_____